THE WORLD FROM MY WINDOW

THE WORLD FROM MY WINDOW

Poems and drawings collected by
George Mendoza
Designed by Alan Peckolick

Hawthorn Books, Inc. Publishers, New York

£ 3.30

133692

This book is dedicated
to the little girl who said:
"But I have no window…"

811.08
Me

"**H**ow well you look! Where have you been?" exclaimed a woman too wealthy for understanding.

"Collecting poems and drawings from poor children all over the United States," I answered simply and honestly.

"For goodness sakes," she replied. "Whatever for?"

"A book called *The World From My Window*."

"Nice title..."—she smiled coldly—"but I'm so tired of all this poverty. It's just being done to death."

"Yes, *they* are," I answered, looking away. "Would you like to hear one of the poems?" And without waiting for her answer, I said: " 'Hey there mister with two cars...why do I have only one shoe?' "

"Oh, I'm so tired having to listen all that...on the television...in the papers...it's dreadful!"

Swallowing my throat, I asked her point blank what good, if any, she had ever done for other human beings.

Proudly she said she had just bought someone a gift of nine signed French plates at an auction bargain of only nine hundred dollars.

"A true bargain!" I blurted. "I hope someone worthy received your gift."

"No," she said, "just my mother-in-law."

Moments later I found myself alone again on the street without any recollection of having said goodbye or it was nice seeing you to the wealthy lady. Now I only felt sick in soul as a man and human being. I thought of all the unforgettable children I had seen over the months and their incredible outpouring of the most beautiful but lonely poetry I had ever seen, and I wondered if their words would ever reach others the way they had reached me. And I wondered about those nine French plates and the kids who probably had nothing to eat at all, and I wanted to hide from myself. As one little girl asked: "Has love run away...?"

To find the children's answer, you must only look within these poems and drawings.

George Mendoza
New York City
August, 1969

I walked across the park
One day. The sun was out
Everything was tired.

The grass was so brown
The grass was so dead,
And the flowers had no desire.

The worms were the
Happiest that day
Because all the fish
Were dead.

Bruce Douglas
Age 16

The only one who understands me is a
Cat named "God"
Who most people only see on Sundays.

Glenn Chinchilla
Age 17

Lonely Walk

When I'm walking down the street,
It seems like footsteps are with me.
When I turn around,
Nothing is there.
Just a shadow when I stare.

Gregory McBride
Age 13

The World

If you picture the world,
As I do,
You'll find that you have,
Discovered a clue,
The ways of magic,
And crimes so tragic,
The distinguished rich,
The poor in a ditch,
Fighting for the country's rights,
Through cold days,
And cold nights,
The rapid way in which it spins,
But our world,
Never ends.

Drenatha Speaks
Age 11

Trees

Trees grow big and tall,
And in the fall the branches are bare,
But the tree is still there.

Renee Johnson
Age 10

Renee Johnson
Age 10

I see the world as a planet of hell.
It began the day I was born,
and the end of hell is death.

Bruce Grayson
Age 15

Based on *City Rhythms*

I was in my house sitting,
And people were hollering.
Car horns were blowing out on the street.
Cats were meowing inside.
Kids tiptoe to hide.
There was a gang meeting out on the street.
Then the telephone rang.
The pots started to bang.
They were picking up the cans out on the street.

I could not stand the noise out on the street.

Lionell McDowell
Age 11

human made shade
stretched out long
with spindly legs and fingers,
black formations
of funny figures,
dancing in a park
absent in the dark
shadows
shadows
or
human
made
shade.

Sharon Clemons
Age 17

I Fear

One day I walked upon the sky and yet the
sun is closest to me I fear I have no
shadow you see.

Kelly Hanis
Age 11

Gregory Corprew
Age 11

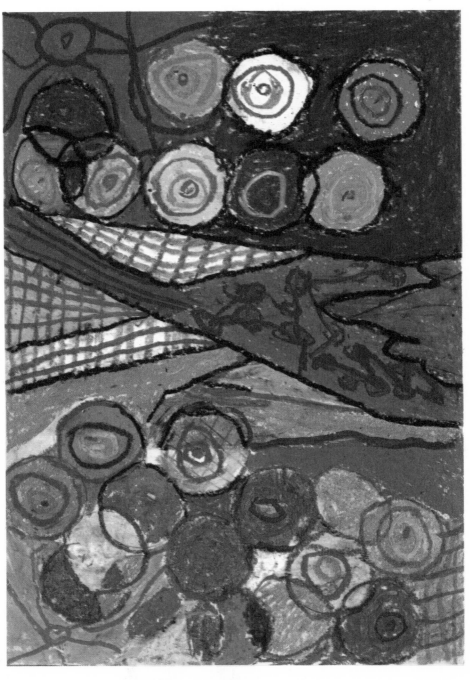

Me

I am me
I am just me
I am a little like other children
But mostly
I am just me

*Mark Giloni
Age 11*

*Kerwin Rivera
Age 6*

The city is big.
The city has black
and white people
And there's one thing
the city doesn't have—
Peace.

*Tyrone Heard
Age 12*

*Alexis Canton
Age 6*

The Most Important

To me,
The most important person
Is me.

Jonetta Taylor
Age 10

Diane Almore
Age 8

New York

slums
dope addicts
projects
protests
strikes
broken down schools

Vaylateena Jones
Age 15

Clothilda Henry
Age 16

I never look out the window
just setting on my bed
I always see everything.
If I can fly
I'll go to the earth
and no one can see me

Jeanette Fincher
Age 12

My World

To me it's not wonderful or good.
It's not fair or satisfactory.
It's bad for me. I have no friends
or anyone that I could trust and depend
on besides my mother. I walk down
the streets alone and wonder why this
seems to be a dark world for me because
I am friendly, quiet and trustworthy...
but this world is too, too dark and since it's
too dark I am invisible. No one can see or
notice me.

Ramonita Diaz
Age 15

The Forgotten Window

People use to look out me,
Now I'm cracked and ugly,
And no one looks out me,
I'm gone forever.

Mark Donohue
Age 12

Rocco Pedatella
Age 7

Im like a balloon in the air
floating around going nowhere.

Im like a ball rolling a round
going everywhere rolling on the ground

Frank Middlebrook
Age 11

Always

I want to do stupid things
like jump over bushes,
play tag with the clouds,
swim in a dry pond,
eat peanut butter, jelly and mayonnaise
sandwiches,
sit on wet grass and stay dry.
Why does someone always say,
"You can't!"

Robert Groppuso
Age 17

Houses have no fun
So you should be happy
That you do

Debby Hendell
Age 11

My Wish

I wish I had
A great big house
Without a sound
Without a mouse

Carliss St
Age 10

Dear Lord,

   Im a resident up here, and I been
wondering. While I was down there a few
months back, and I did a lot of dreamin',
I had thought this was a place of bueaty
and peace, but how can I get some peace
when them people down there sufferin. I
dont want to seem unthankful or ungrateful
but I want to go back. I dont wanna be
dead

W. Mann
Age 16

Mud Puddle

As I look down into this
pool of water and mud,
I see a face
Could it be mine?
I am cold and brown
just like the puddle

Diane Aboulafia
Age 9

Jodi Zohn
Age 5

A Kiss

A kiss is a very important thing by God
To remind a person of your thoughts
A kiss is not as easy to do anytime
But when you find someone...

Ralph Argomaniz
Age 12

Oh Why?

Oh why is it when you're poor
you're hated even more? Oh why, oh why?
Oh why must the rich not want to share
with the sick? Oh why, oh why?
Oh why when you're young you're ruled by the
old ones? Oh why, oh why?
Oh why must we kill to bring death at an
early stage? Oh why, oh why?
Oh why must there be death of pain, to bring
to us shame? Oh why, oh why?
Oh why can't we live without the color of our
skin being such a sin? Oh why, oh why?
Oh why can't we live without the wars of life that
bring death when they fight? Oh why, oh why?

Mary Fletcher
Age 15

I love I love the sun above
if it wasn't so big
I'd call it a light bug

Clay Cox
Age 10

Youth's Question—Revenge's Answer

Hi, Dad,
I met the nicest boy
today.
He's in one of my classes.
Dad, his clothes have holes in them.
Why, Dad?
His hair is different from mine, Dad,
but I think he's nice, Dad.
His skin is darker than mine, Dad.
Dad,
What's a
Nigger?

Nobody, Honey,
Nobody.

Robert Groppuso
Age 17

The Butterfly

Softly
that may not startle
A butterfly
the gentle wind passes
over the old wheat

Julio Benitez
Age 10

Death is when your little world comes to a little nothing.

Arthur Williams
Age 15

Death is when your little world come to a little nothing.

Robert Tato
Age 16

Death is the fear of people.

Jackie Robertson
Age 16

Sadness is a dark feeling inside of your mind.

Ronald Wilson
Age 15

Blindness is an empty world with nothing but your own imagination.

Wayne Driscoll
Age 16

a cat has no tail
but he can run up a tree
if there was no tree
he could not climb
but there is a tree

Betty Williams
Age 10

Little Boy Blue
Come back to school
The world's in a dither
The outlook is cruel
Where is the boy
We are talking about?
He's on the street corner
He's a dropout.

Joe Johnson
Age 11

"What Did You See?"

There's a place by the sea
where I can go when I want to be free
Far from all the lonely people.

I can see what I want to see
there's a seabird high above me
flying with the wind, gracefully.

There's a place by the hillside
where I can go when I want to be free
Far from all the lonely people.

As I sit here I can watch the birds
through my eyes I can see the people
moving about in sorrow.

There's a place down by my street
where I can go when I want to be free
Far from the lonely people.

It's called a graveyard
there's always people around
but no one to help you when
you're down in the ground.

Far from the lonely people.

James Perez
Age 14

Fear is a shade of darkness that overcomes your heart.
Sigfredo Santana
Age 11

Rocco Pedatella
Age 7

rain rain falling down
from the sky
like a diamond in my eye.

Timmy Randle
Age 10

I wonder what the wind would say
If it had a chance to say it
For the wind had seen many a day
And many a hard long year
I wonder what the wind would say
And I wonder what I would hear

Kate Revingston
Age 10

People

People are different as you may know,
When they are happy it is nice,
But they are not always nice,
Especially when they has a knife,
People are also funny,
They will kill for money.

Donald Morris
Age 10

My Magic Window

I have nothing to do
Be it so fine
I am alone
Be it so fine
To my magic window I go, to see the world
All I see is a world of hate
A world of war, a world of hate
But there is a speck of hope
Lovely, wonderful, hope
Hope of love and understanding
Oh Mr. Wind blow not this speck of hope away
For all I wish to see is love
From my magic window

Beverly Carter
Age 11

I See

I see a world hiding from me
Not good, not bad, but in mystery
Its different from mine all nice and sweet
Its trying to hide from me
But I know its there somewhere
Its a real place, I know its there
Our world is just a shadow for it
It must be there somewhere

Ann Jewell
Age 11

A man in Memphis
A non-violent
man in Memphis
A Black
non-violent man in Memphis
Murdered one Thursday
Black Thursday.

Dr. Martin Luther King
black man
taught...preached...lived
non-violence
strived...prayed...died
for human rights

Trumpet of justice and equality
of blacks and browns
Was blown throughout the world.

Pam Crisostomo
Age 14

This old world, this fly dynamite, together, out of sight world is all for loners. When you come in you come alone and when you leave you are still by yourself. To be in a world with others, who are in a world by themselves. To feel wonderful and alive yet to be dead. To be able to go from happiness to sadness without reason. They want to go where they can be what they want to be and have no responsibilities, let the world fly right by without notice. The needles in their arm, the flies in their nose and the pot's in their mouth. Where do they go from here?

Sharon Cooper
Age 15

Smoke

When I look out my window
And all that I see is
Thick black smoke covering me
I see this black smoke
Only when I am sleep
I try to see it when I am awake
But all I see are cars and busses going beep beep

Patrick Murphy
Age 10

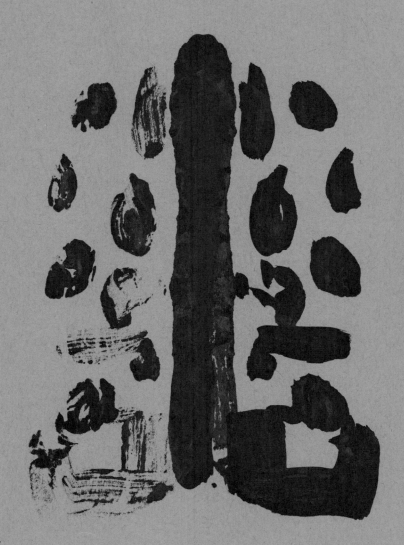

Rocco Pedatella
Age 7

Happiness

The snapping of coal
holds warmth within each chunklet
brings out happiness

Nancy Mitchell
Age 15

Love is a wonderful word.
Love can be hurt in many way.
People have to have love to stay alive.
I believe that love can hurt someone.
I believe that love should stay in the world
for ever and ever.
Because people had love and it run away from them.
There are many people who need love—old folk, children,
ill people.
Many people get married in many different ways in
many different lands.
Many people die without love.
Many people die because the love they had run away.
Love is show in many ways—kiss, smile, and many more.
So try to keep love a wonderful word to everyone
And don't make no more people sad.

Virginia Gory
Age 11

No Reply

My eyes have seen the day and night
My eyes have seen the dark and light
My eyes have seen both good and bad
And now my heart is very sad.

Why must the bad outweigh the good?
Why can't man stand where he once stood?
Where has love gone upon this earth?
Does it die more with each new birth?

Wars are fought and brave men die.
Some people laugh, some people cry
While others stare and stand aside.
I ask you, "Why?"
There's no reply.

Sharon Van Ryte
Age 16

this big rat
i use to know
until
he began to grow
and grow
but he ain't goin
to catch my toe

anon.

Lucille Torres
Age 17

The Mind

A young one's mind is full of peace,
and hopes and cheers
An old one's mind is full of war,
and hatred to last the years

Mark Donohue
Age 12

Life is the greatest disaster and
force of violence I can think of. Sometimes
I wonder, "What are we here for? To lie,
to cheat, to be aggressive, to murder, to
exist in constant fear of what has happened,
what is happening, or what will undoubtedly happen?"
I've found no answer, yet I still believe that
life is the greatest of all types of violence.
Why? Simple! It is the life—the activities,
thoughts, and words of man (and animals) that
make up violence, that keeps its candle burning
endlessly, forever.

If there were no signs of life, no living
creatures of this earth, I honestly believe
that there would be no form of violence—in
the least.

Life is filled with violence. Without
it, life could not survive, at least this is
the impression I've received during my short—
yet very long life span.

Evelyn June Murray
Age 14

I saw someone just like me.
he was black and proud.

Tommie Heard
Age 10

Black nights—
and what did I see?
I saw an angel
black like me.

Ralph Williams
Age 12

Linnette Smith
Age 17

People are all human
When you think about it
But when you don't
They're not

Deborah Hendell
Age 11

If I look out my window
I can see the beautiful grass
and the beautiful things in the world
now I'm going to tell you a poem.

If there was no mother to cook for you
If there was no mother there'll be no Love.
If there was no mother there soon be no
one in this whole world to love.

Carolyn Weaver
Age 11

The World

Oh! can you not see
that you do not understand
all the poverty?

Gloria Abraham
Age 15

Hey there mister
with two cars
why do I have
only one shoe?

anon.

*Mildred Torres
Age 18*

The Devil

The devil lurks on my doorstep while I try to sleep.
No one else can hear him for he's after me.

Wanda Wicks
Age 11

Nature or Man

Along the shores of sand,
Winding along a rolling stream,
Through the forests dark and green,
Nature or man?

Useless destruction, poverty and war,
Vista, missionaries, and the Peace Corp,
Wilderness to cities, water to pollution,
Nature or man?

Floods and storms, city and fire,
Is nature's life-time about to expire,
Or will beauty survive and nature live on,
Nature or man?

Patrick Curry
Age 12

the door

i go in and out of the door
but sometimes the things that happen
outside the door
makes me wish
the door wouldn't open

Reginald Morton
Age 10

Outside

In my window
I'm not scared
But when I leave
I must beware
Beware, Beware, Beware

Charles McDaniels
Age 12

The Dog

I saw a dog limping one day in agony
and pain. I helped the dog thru the
day with a trusted hand and glee. I
felt better that night because I knew
he was healthy and free.

Mitchell Owgang
Age 11

I have a dog once but he die and I started crying

Mack Hines
Age 10

Sometimes I feel
as lonely
as a dog without a master

Yvonne Graham
Age 12

Toni Jackson
Age 9

when night comes
it comes like a black shade
across my heart

Anthony Jones
Age 9

When I Look Outside My Window
or
I Don't Blame It

When I look outside my window,
I see the wall,
It's not a very big wall,
But it's a wall.
It divides the grass from the sidewalk.
I don't blame it.
It seems as if it's protecting the grass
from all city life.
I don't blame it.
Sometimes I go back there to think.
I look at the wall and keep saying:
I don't blame you.
Do you blame it?

Ming-Ming Liu
Age 11

A Door Has Feelings

When you slam me I ake,
All you do is push me around,
Don't you think a door has feelings?

Kelly Hanis
Age 11

Are Things Really Changing?

Fighting Rats and Roaches at Night...
...Hunger by day: I pawn pop
bottles to buy milk and bread.
I STUDY HARDER
I TRY HARDER
only to make something of myself
in America's Society.
BUT CAN I?
Are things changing because I am now
finally recognized as a person—a human
being and not pre-judged because of my
skin color or are things changing because
I am a Black Girl in the Ghetto—and
getting me a job is the only solution to stop
the long hot summer ahead.
Are things really changing for me...
...for my people or is it my
imagination!
Are things REALLY changing?
to you?

Belva Davis
Age 14

Pins, pins falling on the ground
maybe you can hear them
Men, men standing all around
Maybe you may see him.

There is a difference between love
and hate. Half of the world
talks love and the other half
hate.

Gary Thomas
Age 10

Lincoln...Today

Streets are covered with paper
and dirt;
Men are no longer really men.
Children now are in need of drugs.

Black is still and even more
opposite than white.
(will these ever blend?)
Riots come bigger and better, now.

Our proud country can be found
in many parts of the world;
Are you happy?
At least we're one nation, somehow.

Walk on, Abe
Keep walking
I think we're
alone
in this.

Katie Hopkins
Age 16

One day you'll be free
And so will I
We'll take a breath of fresh air
And breathe it in
Someday nobody will be full of guilt
We'll all be free as the birds
We can fly

Laurie Persons
Age 10

I run, I hide,
From this mechanical creation run
by robots.
I find peace for a moment,
I shed a *real* tear, smile
a *real* smile,
Then I am forced back into a phony world.

I'm a fugitive.
An escapee from an eruption
of hatred, bitterness, hostility.
I hide from a world of faceless
images, attached so closely, it
creates an illusion of one.
An illusion?
No!
Because of this I run.

Phyllis Sclafani
Age 16

When I am outside I am
all alone
and when someone walks down the street
I wish I could play with someone
all alone

Norman Blachowski
Age 10

Sometimes I feel
as lonely as a street
without houses.

Kathalena Ray
Age 11

Wilma Friedman
Age 11

I think the things I do wrong.
hate is no word to me
love is the word every one should like.
Then the times it rain it comes
down like full of joy.

Stanley Hardy
Age 11

Little Bird

Take me away with you, please
Let me see all that you see.
Let me for once feel that I am free
Free of the world around me.
To find out just how free will be.
To help me out, just agree.
I have heard so much talk about
Wanting to be free
And I have asked folks what they
were talking about
They didn't know what it means
What it truly means to be free.

Little bird, let me away with you go
Let's not go fast, nor slow
The time we could have, just we know
Little bird, please with you, let me go.

It is not very long that we'll stay
It is not very far that we'll stray
And nothin worldly will I take
To wander in the space of always.

Evelyn June Murray
Age 14

This Soul

This soul is born
This soul will live
This soul must love
This soul must hate
This soul will suffer
This soul will die
This
     soul
         is
             you.

Jim Cendejas
Age 12

On Walking to School

I see bare cold trees
I see junky houses
And condemned stores
I see other children playing
I see old and abandoned cars
And paper all over the ground
Telephone poles and dirt everywhere
Apartment front churches in need of repair
Things should be better
We'll soon have them better

The trees will have leaves
The houses rebuilt
The old, old store will be torn down
The cars will be in good condition
The paper will be picked up
New buildings everywhere around here
Dirt will be only in certain places
The church will be bigger and much better built
Things will be better

Timothy Carter
Age 10

After the black nights
here comes the day
I can see the sun
And the sun will shine on me.

Cheryl McElrath
Age 11

This Summer (July 30, 1968)

This summer wasn't like last summer.
This summer was as stiff as a two by four.
Going around door to door. This summer
I didn't have my lover, didn't bother looking for another.

Christina Jean Smith
Age 16

Independence

You don't care what you do;
You say what's true for you.

You're selfish and unkind;
You say what's on your mind.

You live your life alone;
You're callous as a stone.

They all treat you with scorn;
Why in hell were you born?

Kathleen Begin
Age 16

A Flower

I saw a tiny flower all alone.
This poor little flower was a daisy.
I went over to this flower.
I was going to pick it.
I decided not to even though this poor little flower was alone.

Dona Lea Battiato
Age 11

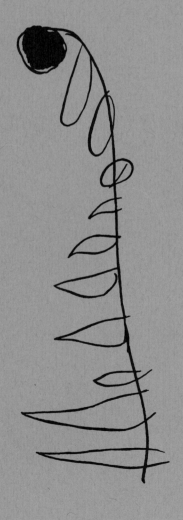

Jodi Zohn
Age 5

Cold

Cold reminds me of a shivering child

All huddled in a corner
It makes me feel all dead inside

Brigit Donohoo
Age 10

A Way of Touching the World

The Ears Are to Hear
A gun shot
A clanging railroad signal
A window breaking
A bomb's exploding
A dog's bark
A roll of thunder
A falling tree
A bell in school
A screeching siren
A dirty joke
A baby's wail
A teacher's teaching
A sweet song
A swat
A funny noise
A cricket singing
A squeak of chalk on the board
The sweet innocent voice of opportunity
All these things the ear can hear.

The Eyes Are to See
A small, swirling dirt tornado
A red, white and blue flag
A dead tree
A car with pink stripes
A hot and vivid bonfire
A dry swamp
A boat on the water
A hurt child
A lonely desert
A bleeding cut
A spooky movie
A glossy bookcover
A homely young girl
A newly-waxed floor
A tottering drunk
A morning star
A depressed face
A fountain lit with colored lights
All are things the eye can see.

Members of the Senior Composition Class
Lincoln High School
Los Angeles, California

What's wrong bird, whats happened
to your wig. Your feathers are falling
apart. I wonder why you are still
flying in the sky.

Minnie Lee Tripplett
Age 11

Races

Races are the colors of people's skin. Well, the kind I'm talking about.

Races are many different colors, red, white, brown and yellow.

I think races should stay together. Some people think differently, but I think we should stay together. As rainbow power. Colors put together.

Do you like how I put in the saying "rainbow power"?

Note: From a letter to President Richard M. Nixon
Rosalind Franklin
Age 11

Nancy Terrell
Age 16

The Clown

The Clown travels with the circus,
He is funny.
But his silliness has a reason.
People act funny,
To be recognized.
But why do they want to be recognized;
They are human, and humans are important.
The Clown has a reason.

Nancy Alexander
Age 9

Lillian Hernandez
Age 7 years 6 months

Sometimes I feel
As lonely as a bird
who can't sing.
He can't express
how he feels.

Brenda Congress
Age 12

Dolores Camacho
Age 10

This house is empty, but people's feelings are still left inside.

Gregory McBride
Age 13

Cathy Wells
Age 11

I wish I could fly so far away
there no boy or girl
can see me

Samuel Hughes
Age 10

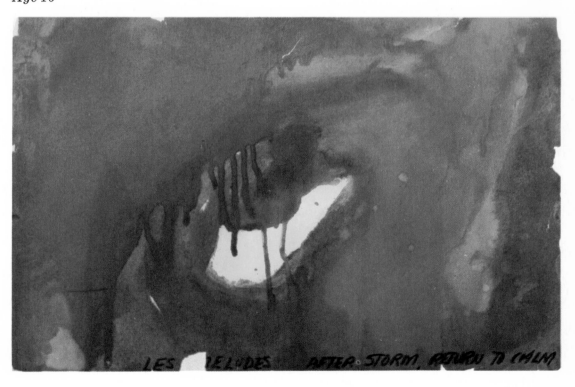

I had a dream

I was dream that I was lost in a goldmine.
I walk and walk till I came to a gold mine shed
and I walk in to the mine shed and it was cold.
I walk in to see the gold in the mine and it was
and I want to get it and come home to be with
my mother.

Michael Bryant
Age 12

Yvette Santiago
Age 6

without children the world would have no joy

Wanda Wicks
Age 11

Gretchen Kapp
Age 7

To Be Alone

I know how it feels to be alone
With no one beside you
When you lie down at bedtime
And think of being all alone
You want to cry

Rebecca Moulder
Age 10

The Boy from Nowhere

The world outside of my window is
like an unknown place
like I'm in space
like I come from out of nowhere

Robert Peace
Age 11

Today Tomorrow?

Oh sure, I live in the city,
But nearer the suburbs than slums.
And my neighborhood seems so friendly
Until the wrong person comes.

Many have moved since July of last summer;
They heard what would happen next.
But before they left they assured us
No outsider would get their old nest.

Since the time the papers quit printing
The rumors came fast and thick.
So my friends and neighbors ran wildly
And bought their own guns real quick.

Now we're guarded against infiltration;
We're armed if they should invade.
Parents keep cautioning children
Who, by now, are deathly afraid.

Steve Cybulski
Age 17

The Men's Turn to Cry

Now I'm alone,
In this world gone cold;
Oh Lord, must I grow old?
As a child I knew no wrong or right,
But now must I lose the fight!

Christine Brzezinski
Age 16

Sometimes I feel
As lonely as a person
in a house with nothing at all
to do
just looking at the walls
just that lonely.

Mitchell Jackson
Age 12

Rocco Pedatella
Age 7

Image Unreal

Pain, darkness followed me homeward.
They crept in with me when i drew the covers over my head.
Arms folded tightly and all around was blackness.
Hands cupped over my ears and all was silent.

Margaret Yee
Age 16

Death !

Death is like a shadow
following close behind,
we never give it much mind,
but it's really there
waiting to overtake you.

Andrew Kack
Age 17

o the world, all the world
is at my feet
but I have no window
to see out

anon.

Animals

There are millions of animals in and out
this world
There's the birds, bees and a small snail
that curls
There's the dog, the cat and the yellow
bumble bee
But when you get right down to it—there's
no animal like me
myself

Linda Anderson
Age 14

George Mendoza represents one of the most independent and unique talents to appear in a long time. Mr. Mendoza is the author of many acclaimed books for children and is the winner of the Lewis Carroll Shelf Award for *The Hunter I Might Have Been*. A native New Yorker, he attended the State University of New York Maritime College for two years and received his B.A. degree from Columbia University. Having always lived near the sea, he learned to sail as a boy and has twice crossed the Atlantic Ocean on a small sloop from New York to England. THE WORLD FROM MY WINDOW marks George Mendoza's twenty-fifth book. Among his other works are: *And I Must Hurry, For the Sea Is Coming In; A Piece of String; The Hawk Is Humming; Flowers and Grasses and Weeds; And Amedeo Asked, How Does One Become a Man?; The Starfish Trilogy; The Sand Poems; To See a Train Go By; A Poem for Putting to Sea; A Wart Snake in a Fig Tree; Fish in the Sky;* and *Herman's Hat*.

Alan Peckolick, a native of New York City, is considered one of today's leading young graphic designers. He is a graduate of Pratt Institute and spent two years with the advertising firm of McCann-Erickson, where he rose to the position of Art Director, working on such major accounts as NBC, Buick, and Coca-Cola. From there he went to Kenyon & Eckhardt and then to design work for Herb Lubalin. In 1966 he was chosen one of the five young up-and-coming American designers, which led to exhibits of his work here and abroad. Mr. Peckolick now is the head of his own graphic-design firm, where he concentrates on films, corporate work, books, and posters. His work has appeared in the New York Art Directors Show and the American Institute of Graphic Arts. At the age of twenty-eight he has received some twenty commendations and awards for the quality of his work. He and his wife, Joan, whom he calls his "inspirational collaborator," and their cocker spaniel reside in the Murray Hill section of Manhattan.

ACKNOWLEDGMENTS

With special thanks to Paul Fargis; Arthur S. T. O'Keefe; Earl Miller, art teacher for the South Bronx Multi-Purpose Supplementary Educational Center; Ruth Sutin, art teacher, Julia Richman High School, New York City; Vilma Krusko, Ruth Hadlow, Pamela Vandemark, Cleveland Public Library; Olga N. Pobutsky and all the contributions from PEER, Detroit Public Library; Emma Plank, Cleveland Metropolitan General Hospital; Joseph L. Buelna, Lincoln Heights Branch Library, Los Angeles; Florence M. Sanborn, Los Angeles Public Library; Mrs. Harriet Covey, Los Angeles County Public Library; LeRoy Hardesty, Principal, Mt. Royal Elementary School, Baltimore; Sara L. Siebert, Enoch Pratt Free Library, Baltimore; Mary Timchick, Cleveland *Press;* Mrs. Joyce Kallir, Principal, P.S. 192, New York City; Mrs. Teddy Olwyler, West Branch Library, Dallas; Miss Judy Kuykendall, Dallas Public Library; George Kaye, Acting Director of Art, Board of Education of the City of New York; Mrs. Cecille Davis, Harriet Ross, The Council on Human Relations, Cleveland; Alan Peckolick, designer; Ruth Sekora; Mrs. Mary N. Woodrich, Cleveland Public School System; Nancy J. Frye, art teacher, Cleveland; and especially to all the children and young adults who shaped the book.